Manukura
The white kiwi

Manukura
The white kiwi

RANDOM HOUSE
NEW ZEALAND

Story by Joy Cowley
Illustrated by Bruce Potter

Kia ora tamariki mā.
My name is Manukura,
which means the Chiefly One,
and my home is Pukaha Mount Bruce.
My guardians are two noble iwi,
Ngāti Manuhiri in the north,
and Rangitāne in the Wairarapa.
People see me as a treasure,
a tohu or special sign
of new beginnings.

Come closer, tamariki,
and I will tell you why.

Behind my story is another story,
so let us start at the beginning.

If you could roll back time
you would find our land full of kiwi.

But then came the enemies,
the dogs, the ferrets and stoats,
the fires that cleared the forests.
The kiwi are becoming extinct.
How can they be saved?

At Pukaha Mount Bruce,
kiwi eggs are hatched
in an incubator.

The baby kiwi are fed
until they are big enough
to look after themselves,
then they are released
in the great Pukaha forest,
protected from predators.

With the help of Ngāti Manuhiri,
thirty brown kiwi were taken
from Hauturu, Little Barrier Island,
and released in the forest
at Pukaha Mount Bruce.

This is where my story begins.
Two of those birds from Hauturu
are my mother and father.

I have no memory of being moved
from the forest to the hatchery.
I was a little blob in a large egg,
feeding on the rich yolk
and growing, growing
for seventy to eighty days.

On the outside, my shell
looked like all the others.
No one at the hatchery knew
what was happening inside.

It is May 2011.
Twelve eggs have hatched,
all North Island brown kiwi.
I am number thirteen
and I know it is my time.
Tap, tap! The end of my beak
is strong for making a hole
in the hard shell. Tap, tap!

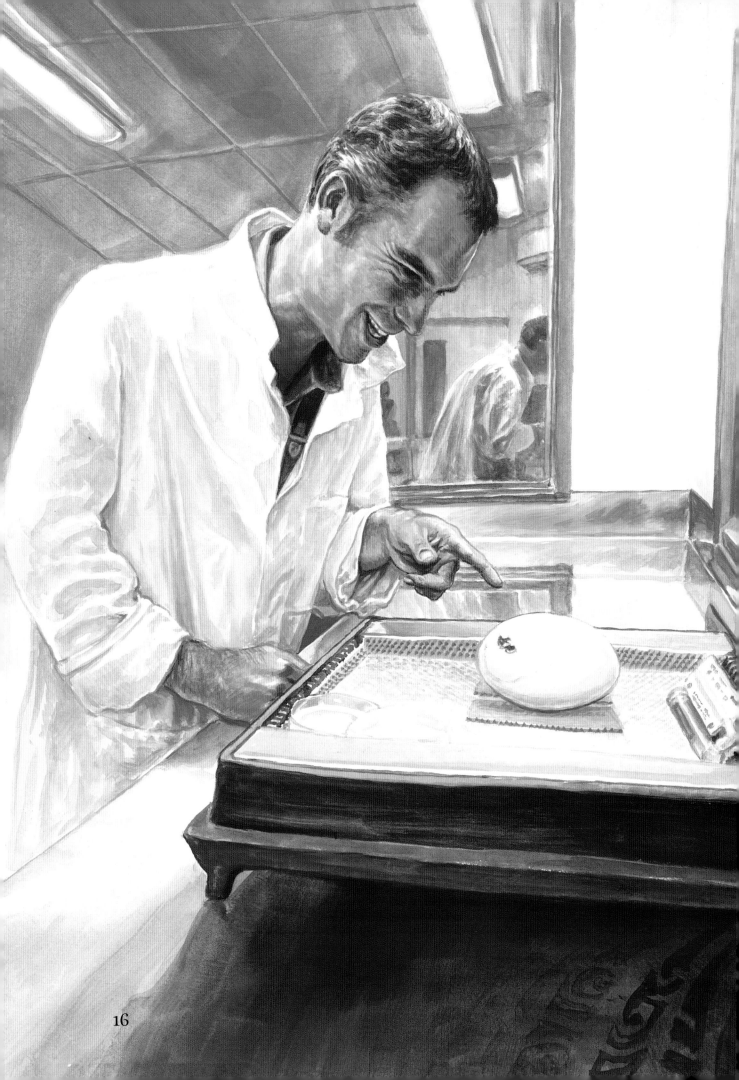

Ranger Darren thinks he can see
a white feather in the hole.
He knows that the kiwi
on Hauturu, Little Barrier Island,
sometimes have a white feather
in their brown plumage.

But I have a bigger surprise
for the world.

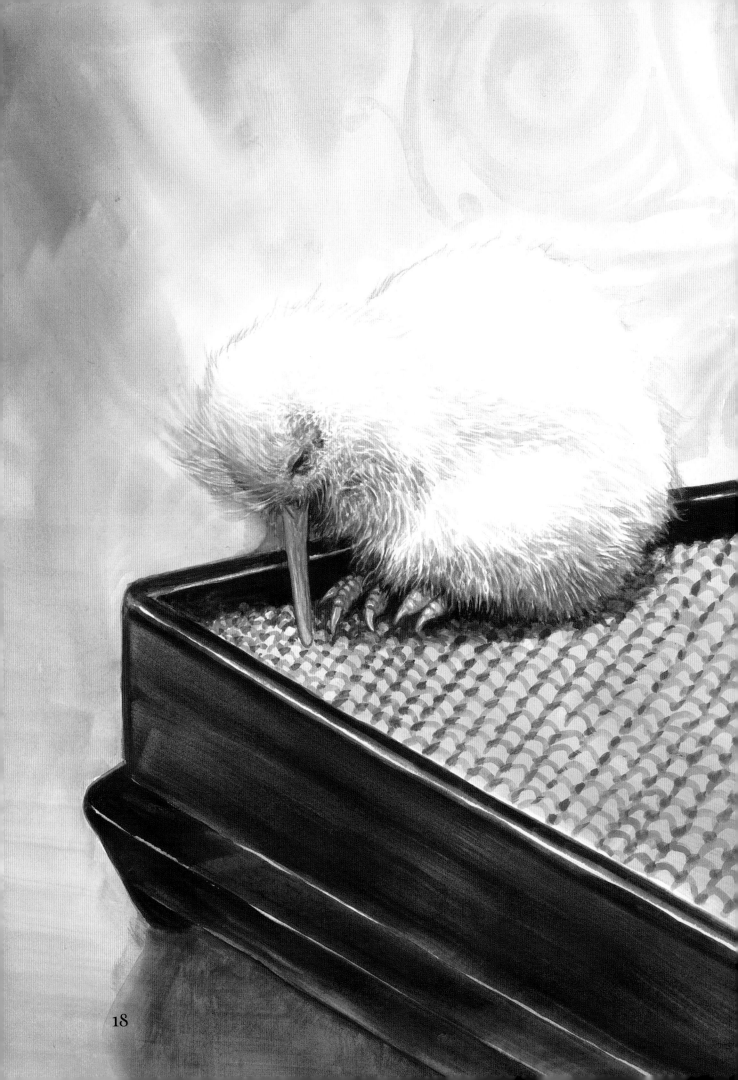

All my feathers are snowy white.

No, I am not an albino,
a creature lacking colour.
I am the rarest of birds,
a pure white kiwi.
My feathers are like snow,
like sea foam on the shore,
like moonlight on the land.

I am a girl
and I've come with a message.

Jason of Rangitāne says,
"Every now and then
something extraordinary
comes along to remind us
how special life is."

Here at the sanctuary
I get visitors from distant lands.
The world is eager to know about me,
but I am happy to spend my days
with my brown-feathered friend Pōtiki,
who was egg number fourteen.
She, too, is special.

So are you, tamariki!
Think how special you are!
Ever since this world began
there has never been a person
exactly the same as you,
and there never will be again.

Manukura, the white kiwi,
comes to remind you
that you too, are a taonga,
and the world is made better
by the unique treasure
that you are.

Kiwi Facts

- Female kiwi weigh up to 3kg. Males weigh up to 2kg, females are bigger to accommodate their huge egg. A kiwi egg takes up about 20% of the female's body.

- Manukura weighed 280g at hatch. Pōtiki weighed 340g at hatch. The hatch weight of kiwi is usually 320–350g.

- The hatchling, nourished with yolk, does not eat for about five days and is then fed a special captive diet. The young kiwi have worms and insects topped up with ox heart, vegetables, bananas and other nutrients.

- It takes up to 6 months for a juvenile kiwi to reach the release weight of 1.2kg.

- Female kiwi are generally more aggressive than males and, being larger, are harder to handle.

- Kiwi reach breeding age at 2–3 years.

- Kiwi have a lifespan of approximately 30 years.

Pukaha Mount Bruce — National Wildlife Centre

Pukaha Mount Bruce is situated north of Masterton, in the Wairarapa and Tararua districts of the North Island of New Zealand.

Visitors to the sanctuary can get close to the country's unique ecological history. The experience includes eel and kākā feeding, a kiwi nocturnal house, kiwi chick rearing in season, tuatara, forest walks, bird viewing, films and ranger talks.

The restoration of wildlife in the 940-hectare Pukaha native forest began in 2001, with the reintroduction of endangered native birds.

The sanctuary is protected from predators by more than 1000 traps which are monitored on a day-to-day basis.

The success of pest control management has meant that kōkako, kiwi and kākā are now breeding in the wild.

For more information: www.pukaha.org.nz
Video: http://www.vimeo.com/jetproductions.manukura

A RANDOM HOUSE BOOK published by Random House New Zealand
18 Poland Road, Glenfield, Auckland, New Zealand

For more information about our titles go to www.randomhouse.co.nz

A catalogue record for this book is available from the National Library of
New Zealand

Random House New Zealand is part of the Random House Group
New York   London   Sydney   Auckland   Delhi   Johannesburg

First published 2012

© 2012 story Joy Cowley, illustrations Bruce Potter
Photos on page 31 by Mike Heydon

The moral rights of the author have been asserted

ISBN 978 1 86979 838 3

Design: Bruce Potter and Megan van Staden
Printed in China by Everbest Printing Co Ltd